JUST LIKE YOU!

Yes, all little boys are different

... but there is one time when they

are all alike. At the end of each day

every little boy likes to climb

on Mommy's or Daddy's lap, say his

prayers, then snuggle down to sleep

in his cozy bed ...

Some like to explore,

and some like to read

and pretend.

and others who like the rain.

There are some little boys

who like the snow . . .

. . . and build things.

They like to collect things

Little boys like to sail

boats, play marbles ... and

tease little girls.

and they all like to play.

They like to climb trees,

walk on fences

or fly kites.

They all go to school . . .

There are little boys who

have sisters and brothers...

and there are little boys

who have none.

Some live in friendly houses in

small towns, and others live

in large houses in great big cities.

Some are plump,

some are thin,

and some are

in-between.

It is very strange about little boys . . .

God makes them all, yet they are

as different as can be.

Little Boys

Words and Pictures by Stina Nagel

The C. R. Gibson Company
Norwalk, Connecticut

From Aunties Donna + Darleen

My Book

John William
Gotschall